The DOCTOR WHO

MONSTER BOOK

BY TERRANCE DICKS

Designed by Brian Boyle A.R.C.A.,

Printed in Great Britain by
Hunt Barnard Printing Ltd, Aylesbury, Bucks

Target Books are published by
Tandem Publishing Ltd,
14 Gloucester Road, London SW7 4RD

A Howard & Wyndham Company

CONTENTS

WHO IS TH

DOCTOR?

The mysterious traveller in Time and Space known only as **'The Doctor'** first made his appearance on our television screens over ten years ago. At that time we knew almost nothing about him. One of the purposes of this book is to piece together the Doctor's history from what we have learned over the years.

When we first met the Doctor he appeared to be somewhere in his sixties, a little stiff and crochety, but still spry, vigorous and alert. His frock-coat, check trousers and high stiff collar made him look rather like the popular picture of an eccentric Victorian professor. He was accompanied by a young girl, Susan, who called him 'grandfather' and he travelled through Time and Space in a marvellous, but sometimes erratic, machine called the **Tardis.**

The name *Tardis* is made up of the initial letters from 'Time and Relative Dimensions in Space'. The *Tardis looked* like a Police Call Box, a special dark-blue telephone kiosk from which police or members of the public could call for assistance. This was because the *Tardis*, when in full working order, has the power to change its shape into some object which would blend into its surroundings. Unfortunately, this chameleon mechanism got stuck on the first visit to Earth, and the Doctor has never got round to repairing it. So the *Tardis* has remained in the same shape ever since, even though this kind of Police Box is now obsolete.

Inside, the *Tardis* is a fantastically advanced craft which can travel through Space and Time. The most astonishing thing about the *Tardis* is the fact that it's bigger on the inside than on the outside — a fact which the Doctor sometimes explains by muttering crossly that it is 'dimensionally transcendental'.

Although still very active, with a great appetite for knowledge and adventure, this first Doctor was already showing some signs of his great age. He could be querulous and irritable, impatient with those whose intelligence didn't match his own. He was capable of a kind of childish secretiveness and selfishness. Once, on a dangerous alien planet, he endangered the lives of his companions by deliberately sabotaging the *Tardis* because he wished to stay and explore.

But despite his failings, the Doctor was still a formidable character. His quick wits and his courage carried him, together with a variet of companions, through numerous exciting adventures on Earth (past and future) and on many alien worlds.

At the end of an adventure with the terrible

Cybermen, the Doctor casually announced that his old body was beginning to 'wear out'. He collapsed into a coma, and his astonished companions saw him begin to change . . . When he recovered, he was, literally, a different man.

For a start he looked much younger. Moreover, his temperament had changed with his appearance.

This Doctor was a strange, elusive character, gentle and wayward with a whimsical charm. The arrogance of his previous incarnation had vanished and he was modest and unassuming. His clothes became more extravagant and eccentric, he played the flute, and sometimes he wore extraordinary hats. But beneath this rather clownish exterior the Doctor's brilliant mind and forceful personality were unchanged, and in the adventures that followed this odd-looking little man was to save the day in many a terrifying crisis.

The Doctor retained this form through many exciting adventures. Then, at last, he encountered the terrible War Lords, who were attempting a Galactic conspiracy so vast and terrifying that even the Doctor had to ask for help. It was now that we began to learn a little more about his past. The Doctor, it appeared, was a kind of renegade, a maverick member of an immensely advanced and powerful race. The Time Lords had gained the power to travel in Space and Time, as well as to regenerate their own bodies when threatened by old age or illness. It was a part of their philosophy that they must use their powers to observe the affairs of the Universe, but never to intervene. The Doctor, however, was convinced that it was necessary at least to *try* to right some of the Galaxy's many wrongs. He had stolen the *Tardis* and fled to roam the Universe, struggling against evil when and wherever he encountered it. But in this final crisis, he was forced to turn to his own people for help, even though he knew that to do so would mean recapture.

The conspiracy of the War Lords was frustrated, but in the process the Doctor was taken prisoner by his own people and put on trial before the High Court of the Time Lords. Unrepentantly, he made a moving speech, claiming that it was the moral duty of the Time Lords to help the weak and oppressed, to use their powers to struggle against evil as he had done.

Although he was finally found guilty, the Doctor's plea was not without its effect. His sentence was a comparatively light one, a period of exile on the planet Earth in the twentieth time zone. It is interesting to note that the Doctor's rebellion brought about a gradual shift in the policy of the High Council of the Time Lords. From this point they were to intervene more and more in the affairs of the Galaxy, often using the Doctor as their sometimes unwilling agent.

Indeed the Doctor's exile was in itself an example of this change. The Time Lords must have been aware that the exile would coincide with a time of great crisis for Earth. On his arrival the Doctor became immediately involved in the first Auton invasion, and many other alien attacks on Earth were to follow.

As part of the Doctor's sentence the Time Lords decided that there should be yet another change in his appearance. The Doctor who arrived on Earth was very different from the comic little rebel who had defied the Court of the Time Lords.

This new Doctor was a more obviously heroic figure than in his previous incarnations. He was tall, lean and elegant, with a handsome lined face, and a shock of white hair. His taste in clothes was flamboyant, running to frilled shirts, velvet smoking jackets and elaborate cloaks.

He was very much the man of action, dashing, impulsive with a ready charm. Although he never carried weapons, apart from his multi-purpose sonic screwdriver, he was a master of Venusian Aikido, one of the few two-armed beings to master this most deadly of Martial Arts.

One of the new Doctor's strongest characteristics was a passion for all kinds of gadgetry, and for any new and original form of transport. His souped-up Edwardian roadster, **'Bessie'** was a typical example. Later the Doctor acquired his **'Whomobile'** a futuristic-looking vehicle something between a racing car and a flying saucer, with the ability to take to the air in times of crisis. In the course of his adventures, the Doctor drove speedboats, hovercraft, and even a one-man helicopter.

Perhaps the most extraordinary adventure of this period involved the Doctor in a confrontation with his two former selves. The Time Lords decided that no less than three Doctors were needed to deal with the renegade Time Lord **Omega,** and lifted the Doctor's earlier selves from their proper Time Streams so that he could literally help himself.

13

The collaboration began amiably enough but it didn't stay like that. The third Doctor clashed immediately with his previous incarnation, and although they eventually succeeded in defeating Omega, their collaboration was a stormy one, with the original Doctor often acting as peacemaker.

It was as a result of this particular adventure that the Time Lords lifted the Doctor's sentence of exile, restoring his freedom to roam Time and Space once more. Ironically, this new freedom eventually led to the end of the Doctor's third incarnation.

On a trip to Metebelis Three, famous Blue Planet of Acteon Galaxy, the Doctor acquired one of the planet's famous blue crystals as a souvenir. Unfortunately, this particular crystal formed an important part of the plans of the giant **Spiders,** ruthless rulers of the planet. Returning to Metebelis, the Doctor was forced to enter the cave of the Great One, their all-powerful Ruler, and although he succeeded in destroying her, his body became riddled with the deadly alien radiation of her cave. There was only one way to save his life — the Doctor had to change his appearance yet again . . .

And so the Doctor entered on his fourth incarnation,
looking as different from the first three as they did
from each other. But in spite of this difference in
appearance, the latest Doctor blends all the qualities
of the three that have gone before. The strong will
and brilliant scientific brain of the first,
the inconsequential humour of the second, the
warmth and charm of the third. A strange
mixture of contradictory qualities, genius
and clown, hero and buffoon, he is well
equipped to face the many exciting adventures
that lie before him. Now it is time to take
a look at some of the monsters that have
attacked the Doctor throughout his many lives . . .

15

THE MONSTERS

...THE WORST CAME FIRST!

THE DALEKS

It is surely no coincidence that the first of the many hostile alien life-forms that the Doctor was to encounter was also the most vicious, the most deadly, and the most persistent — the dreaded **Daleks.**

The Doctor first encountered the Daleks when the *Tardis* landed on their home planet of Skaro, where the Daleks were locked in conflict with their hereditary enemies, the Thals. Both sides were survivors of a terrible atomic war that had left their planet contaminated by deadly radiation. The **Thals** had developed protective drugs to counteract the effects, but the Daleks had built themselves protective metal casings. Genetic engineering and generations of mutation had transformed their bodies until an unbearably hideous creature was left living inside an armoured shell. Unfortunately, the Daleks had by now lost all human feeling and compassion. They had evolved into a race of ruthless killers, their watchword the harsh, metallic cry **'Exterminate'!**

In a final battle on Skaro, the Doctor thought he had destroyed the Daleks, but he could seldom have been more wrong. The Daleks struck at Earth itself, invading London and turning human beings into their slaves in a plot to steal the planet itself. After

another encounter with the Daleks on the planet Kembel where he defeated them by activating a Time Destructor, the Doctor encountered them on Vulcan. The first task for the Doctor's second incarnation was to defeat their attempt to take over the Earth Colony.

For their next attack, the Daleks turned once more to Earth, cunningly going back to the Victorian age to conceal their assault. Once again the Doctor tracked them down, following them to Skaro to defeat them. The Daleks' next attack upon Earth was successful — at least for a time. They attacked after Earth had weakened itself by a terrible atomic war, and took over a world too weak to resist them. The Doctor, now exiled on Earth in his third incarnation, became aware of this when human resistance-fighters returned to the twentieth century from the Dalek-dominated Earth of the future in an attempt to change their own history. The Doctor followed the guerillas into the future where he found Daleks ruling the enslaved population of a ruined Earth, aided by their savage ape-like servants, the **Ogrons.** The Doctor defeated the Daleks, thus returning human history to its proper course.

The Doctor's next two encounters with the Daleks were both to take place on alien worlds. First, on the planet Spiridon, he enlisted the help of Spiridon's invisible inhabitants, and a commando party of Thals, to destroy an immense army of Daleks held on the planet in cold storage for a projected invasion of the galaxy.

The Doctor's next battle with the Daleks took place on the savage and terrifying planet of **Exxilons.** Here, humans and Daleks were struggling for possession of a drug which could cure the space plague which threatened to wipe out every living creature in the Galaxy. Doctor, humans, and Daleks alike were attacked by the planet's hostile inhabitants.

Eventually the Doctor enlisted the help of a more friendly species of native to defeat the Daleks' plans, and worked with **Bellal.** It was not until his fourth incarnation that the Doctor was to encounter the Daleks yet again. At the urging of the Time Lords he journeyed to the planet Skaro at a time just *before* the Daleks were created by the ruthless crippled scientist **Davros,** in an attempt to defeat the Thals. He almost succeeded in his task, but events were too strong for him and the Daleks survived. Doubtless they will continue their determined attempts to conquer the Galaxy and destroy the Doctor!

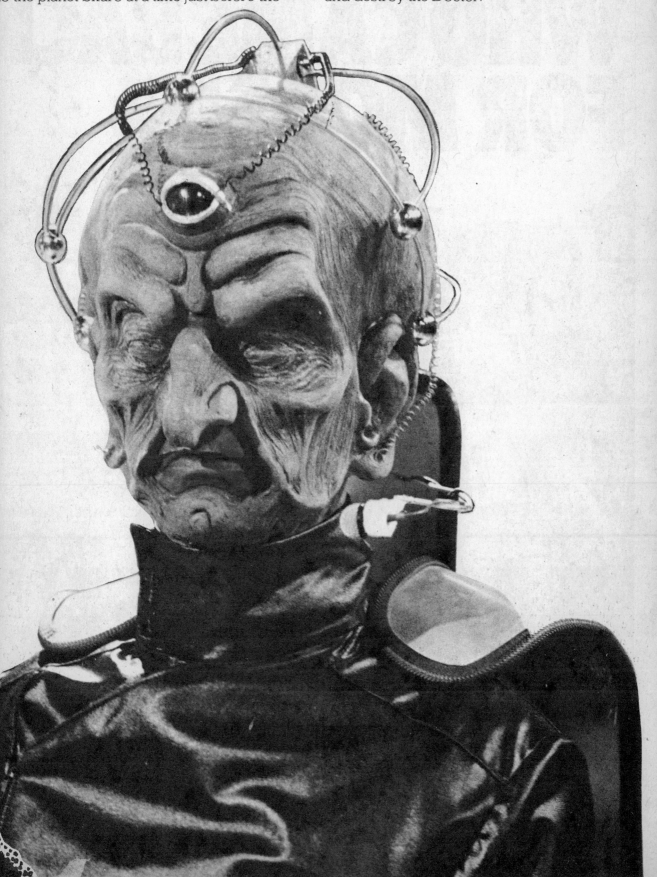

MONSTERS WHO CAME BACK FOR MORE!

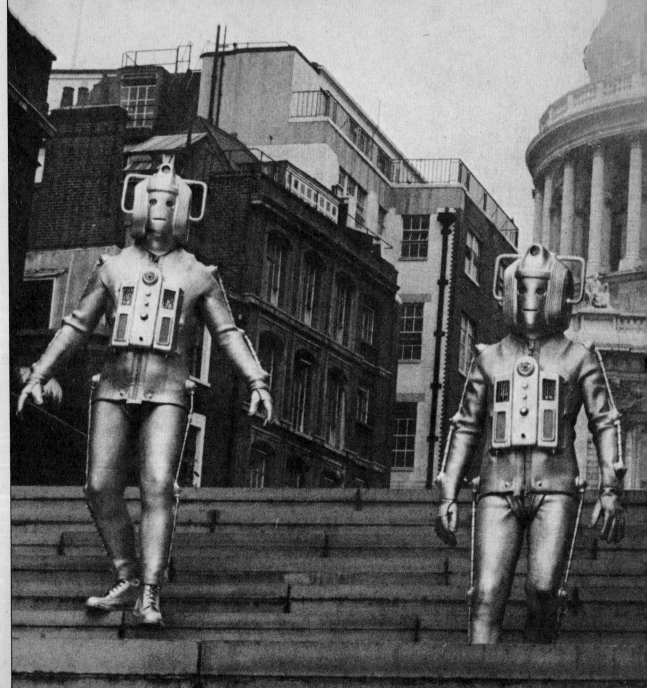

THE CYBERMEN

As we have seen, the Doctor had quite a number of clashes with the Daleks. There were other enemies who returned to the attack after a first defeat, in particular the ruthless, emotionless silver giants known as **Cybermen.** Once humanoid in form, the Cybermen had increased their strength and longevity by replacing limbs and organs of flesh and blood with metal and plastic, losing all human feeling and compassion in the process. In the last adventure of his first incarnation the Doctor foiled their attempt to take over a Space Tracking Station at the South Pole.

Their next attempt was an attack on a Weather Station on the Moon, and the Cyberman menace was later revived by a rash archeologist excavating the Tomb of the Cybermen.

Later, the Cybermen returned for a third attack upon Earth, enlisting the help of a power-mad Earth scientist. They infiltrated London by hiding in its sewers — following this up with a full-scale attack in force. In his fourth incarnation the Doctor met the Cybermen once more, this time enlisting the help of the **Vogans** in defeating their attempt to take over a Space Station.

THE ICE WARRIORS

The giant scaly-green **Ice Warriors,** a savagely militaristic race from Mars, also returned to plague the Doctor more than once. The first Ice Warrior was discovered buried deep in the ice during the Earth's second Ice Age. At first taken for a buried Viking, the creature proved to be the Captain of a Martian Space ship, attacking the humans savagely once revived.

In a later adventure, the Ice Warriors, like so many other hostile alien life-forms, planned the conquest of Earth, spearheading their attack with an invasion of a base on the moon, from which they despatched a lethal fungus which altered Earth's weather.

When this attempt was also defeated the Ice Warriors withdrew their attention from Earth. The Doctor's subsequent encounters with them concerned the affairs of the planet Peladon, a world emerging from barbarism to claim membership of the Galactic Federation. In his first visit to Peladon, the Doctor, to his own astonishment, found himself *allied* with the Ice Warriors in defeating reactionaries who wanted to keep Peladon out of the Federation. But on the Doctor's second visit, the Ice Warriors had reverted to their old militaristic ways, plotting to seize control of the planet in an attempt to gain control of its valuable mineral deposits.

25

In both these adventures, **Aggedor,** the
sacred beast of Peladon, played a large part.
In the first, the beast was used by an
unscrupulous High Priest to destroy his enemies.
Aggedor was later tamed by the Doctor. In the second, a
villainous miner used advanced technology to produce a
'ghost' Aggedor which struck terror into the natives of Peladon.

THE YETI

Yeti is of course the traditional name of the Abominable Snowman, the mysterious creature rumoured to roam the mountains of Tibet. But the Yeti encountered by the Doctor were Robots, created by an evil Alien Intelligence to drive away the simple Tibetan monks from their monastery.

Defeated by the Doctor, the Intelligence later struck again, this time using the Yeti to attack London. The Doctor found himself fighting them in the incongruous setting of the London Underground system.

THE AUTONS

Like the Yeti, the **Autons** were really only the weapons used by the Doctor's real enemy, in this case the formless *Nestenes* with their sinister affinity for all kinds of plastic. The Autons were living plastic dummies, some crude and unfinished, some completely accurate replicas of human beings. In their second attack the Autons were mostly disguised as harmless carnival figures, though the malignant Nestene consciousness used such diverse objects as an armchair, a doll, a telephone cord and a host of plastic daffodils, in their endeavours to kill the Doctor and conquer Earth. This time they were aided by the **Master,** a renegade Time Lord and an old enemy of the Doctor's who was to return to trouble him in many later adventures.

THE SILURIANS

These giant reptiles were the survivors of a reptilian civilisation which flourished on Earth long before the rise of Man. Accidentally revived from their long hibernation by the operations of an underground research centre, the **Silurians** set about re-conquering 'their' Earth, now overrun by that upstart ape called man.

One of their weapons was a dinosaur, preserved from the time of their rule, and now used as the guardian of their secret underground base.

THE SEA DEVILS

The **Sea-Devils** were marine cousins of the Silurians. *Their* base was hidden beneath the ocean, and they were awakened by the drilling operations of off-shore oil rigs, which they promptly destroyed, as a first step in the re-conquest of Earth.

—ACHILLEOS—

THE SONTARANS

The Doctor has so far had two encounters with the **Sontarans,** a savage extra-terrestial race whose one interest is constant warfare. Strangely enough the first meeting took place in the medieval period of Earth's history. **Lynx,** captain of a crashed Sontaran space-ship, persuaded Irongron, the local Robber Baron to help him, paying for aid by equipping the Baron's soldiers with modern weapons. The Doctor journeyed back into the past to stop this interference with history. His next struggle with a Sontaran occurred on the polluted and uninhabited Earth of the distant future. The Sontarans, warlike as ever, were planning to test the possible resistance of humanity to a Sontaran attack. This time the Doctor found himself in conflict with **Field-Major Steyr,** a typically ruthless Sontaran officer, who was using human captives as the subjects for his cruel experiments.

A 'MIXED BAG' OF MONSTERS

Not *all* of the Doctor's enemies returned to plague him again and again. Some were decisively destroyed on the first encounter. Others, so far at least, have never crossed his path again — the universe after all is vast, and contains uncounted intelligent life-forms. Here, then, is a selection of the monsters and alien beings the Doctor has so far encountered only once, none the less memorable for their single appearances.

THE ZARBI

These giant ant-like creatures existed in a state of perpetual warfare with the **Menoptera,** butterfly-like fellow inhabitants of the planet Vortis. The Doctor brought about a reconciliation, so that the two very different species could live together in peace.

THE SENSORITES

When the *Tardis* landed on a giant space-ship, the Doctor discovered its crew to be under the mental control of the **Sensorites,** a race of telepathic aliens who lived on a planet called Sense-Sphere. The past experience of the Sensorites left them hostile to humanity and the Doctor tracked down the renegade humans causing the trouble.

THE MECHANOIDS

The **Mechanoids** were Robots,
inhabitants of the jungle planet Mechanus.
The Doctor narrowly escaped death when he
became involved in a battle between the
Mechanoids, armed with their flame-throwing
guns, and his old enemies the Daleks.

THE AXONS

The **Axons** were a race of space travelling parasites who lived by attaching themselves to other planets and draining them of their energy. They arrived on Earth as beautiful golden beings, but turned into savage many-tentacled monsters when the Doctor exposed their true aims.

THE MINING ROBOT

The Time Lords despatched the *Tardis* to a distant planet where a ruthless mining corporation was trying to scare off colonists with a series of faked monster attacks.

The Doctor discovered that the attacks were carried out by a mining robot equipped with claws, though he himself was nearly killed in making this discovery.

The situation worsened with the arrival of the Doctor's old enemy, the Master, who was searching for a long-hidden Doomsday Weapon which would give him control of the Galaxy. The Doctor foiled the Master's plans with the help of the **Guardian,** sole survivor of the super-race that had built the weapon.

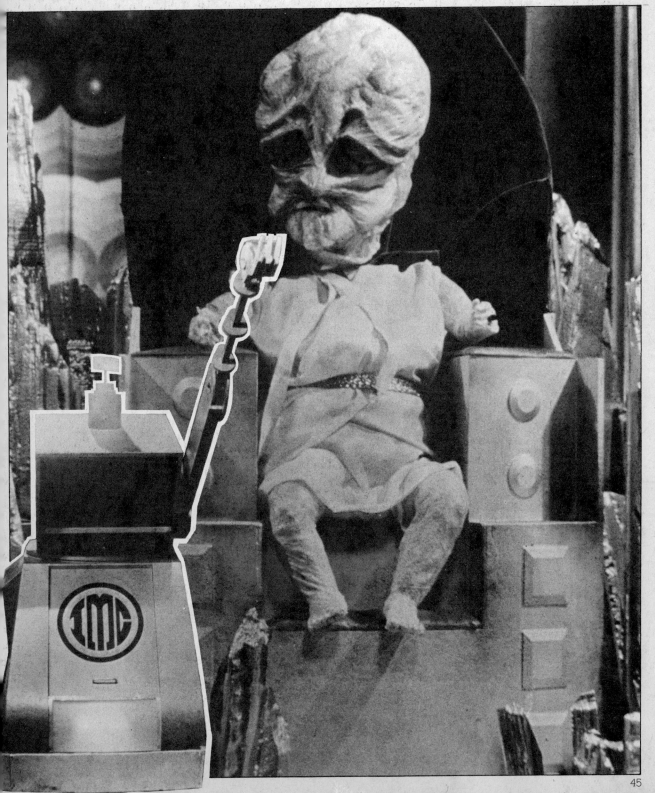

THE DAEMONS

Azal was a member of a race known as the **Daemons.** They had visited Earth long ago and assisted mankind on the path of developing intelligence. Awakened from his long sleep, Azal was poised between handing on his great powers, or destroying a planet which seemed to him a failed experiment.

The Doctor, in an adventure which mixed occult powers with alien science, struggled to prevent the Master from gaining Azal's power, and tried to persuade Azal to let mankind work out its own destiny. . . **Bok,** a church gargoyle, was brought to life by Azal's power.

OMEGA

As you read earlier, it took no less than *three* Doctors to defeat the renegade Time Lord **Omega,** though the brunt of the struggle fell on the Doctor's second and third incarnations.

Their task was made more difficult by the hideous **Gellguards,** blobby, almost shapeless servants of Omega, sent to kidnap them from Earth . . .

THE DRACONIANS

Not really monsters as such, the **Draconians** were a proud, intelligent, and belligerent space-travelling race. They came into conflict with man when both species were spreading their respective empires through the stars. Man and Draconian clashed almost immediately, perhaps because they were so much alike in temperament. They narrowly escaped becoming locked in a terrible space-war, largely provoked by the machinations of the evil Master, aided by his Ogron servants, and guided by his current employers, the Daleks. By exposing the plot to provoke war, the Doctor paved the way for peace between humanity and the Draconians.

GIANT MAGGOTS

Industrial pollution bred the **Green Death,** a killer slime spread by a race of giant maggots, mutations spawned in an abandoned Welsh mine, which eventually changed into **giant flies.**

The Doctor battled with those responsible for the spread of the menace, a ruthless chemical firm whose super-efficient computer, called Boss, had actually taken over the running of the entire company.

PREHISTORIC MONSTERS

A band of renegade scientists had driven away the population of London by scooping up monsters from the prehistoric past and depositing them in the present day.

The Doctor found himself attacked by a variety of pre-historic creatures. The largest was the **tyrannosaurus rex**, but one of the most vicious was a **pterodactyl** that attacked him in a deserted garage . . .

THE SPIDERS

The giant **Spiders** of Metebelis Three held the planet's human inhabitants in slavery. A blue crystal, originally taken from the planet by the Doctor, was vital to the plans of their rulers, and the Spiders came to Earth to recover it, teleporting themselves over the vast distances of space. Sarah Jane Smith, the Doctor's assistant, saw one of the creatures arrive, and later came for a time under their control…It was in this adventure that the Doctor's body became so badly damaged by radiation that he had to change his shape once again…

THE GIANT ROBOT

When the Robot grew to giant size, it went on a killer rampage and had finally to be destroyed by the Doctor. Sarah couldn't help shedding a few tears at its ending.

The **Giant Robot** was the first menace the Doctor had to face in his fourth incarnation. Far from evil in itself, the Robot had been corrupted and misused by its own maker, and used as a weapon by a group of arrogant scientists in quest of world domination.

Sarah, the Doctor's assistant, felt a strange affinity for the giant metal creature, sensing in it the simplicity and nobility led astray by its evil controllers. The Robot seemed to return this sympathy, and Sarah's understanding of the Robot saved the Doctor's life.

THE WIRRN

This giant telepathic ant-like creature attempted to take over a space station which held, suspended in cold storage, all the future population of Earth. One of the creatures merged with a human being, and it was by appealing to the remnants of humanity in the monstrous body of the hybrid creature, that the Doctor was able to save the day.

THE ZYGONS

Beneath the murky waters of Loch Ness, the **Zygons** lay waiting for hundreds of years, struggling to repair their wrecked space-ship. In the waters of the loch roamed the **Skarasen,** a fearsome beast brought by the Zygons from their home planet. Occasionally spotted by humans throughout the years, the Skarasen became known as the Loch Ness Monster.

When the Zygons learned their home world had been destroyed, they decided to take over the Earth and transform it into a replica of their own planet. In the final struggle, the Doctor was forced to destroy the Zygons and their space-ship, but the monster survived to live happily on in Loch Ness.

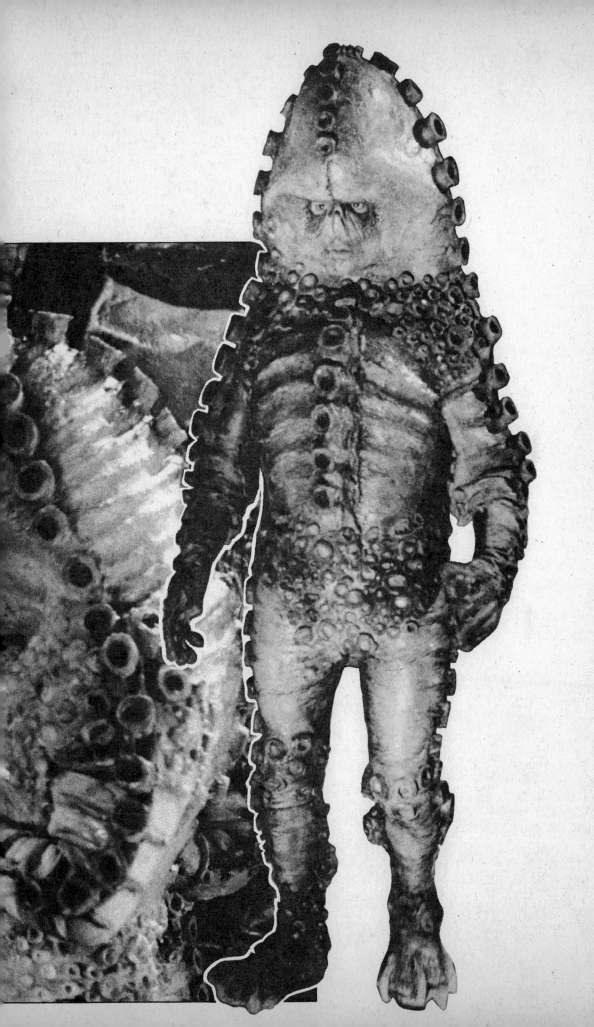

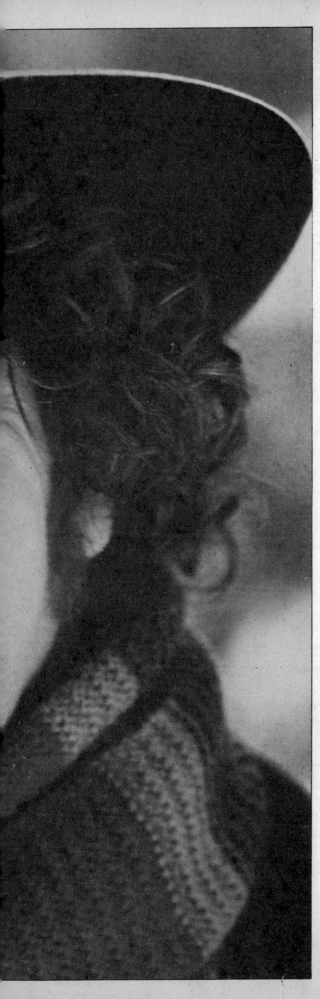

These are some of the monsters the Doctor has faced during his many lives and long career. Who knows what terrors and dangers lie before him? One thing is certain — he will be faced with the return of some old enemies and the arrival of many terrifying new ones.

Television Credits
DOCTOR WHO
played by

William Hartnell

Patrick Troughton

Jon Pertwee

Tom Baker

THE MONSTERS created by

DALEKS ... Terry Nation
CYBERMEN ... Kit Pedler and Gerry Davis
ICE WARRIORS ... Brian Hayles
YETI ... Mervyn Haisman and Henry Lincoln
THE AUTONS ... Robert Holmes
SILURIANS AND SEA DEVILS ... Malcolm Hulke
SONTARANS ... Robert Holmes
THE ZARBI ... Bill Strutton
THE SENSORITES ... Peter R. Newman
THE MECHANOIDS ... Terry Nation
THE AXONS ... Bob Baker and Dave Martin
THE DAEMONS ... Robert Sloman
MINING ROBOT AND GUARDIAN ... Malcolm Hulke
OMEGA ... Bob Baker and Dave Martin
DRACONIANS ... Malcolm Hulke
GIANT MAGGOTS ... Robert Sloman
SPIDERS ... Robert Sloman
GIANT ROBOT ... Terrance Dicks
WIRRN ... Robert Holmes
ZYGONS ... Robert Banks Stewart
EXXILONS ... Terry Nation
DAVROS ... Terry Nation
BELLAL ... Terry Nation
LYNX ... Robert Holmes
OGRONS ... Louis Marks
GELLGUARDS ... Bob Baker and Dave Martin
STEYR ... Bob Baker and Dave Martin
VOGANS ... Kit Pedler and Gerry Davis
THE MONSTER OF PELADON ... Brian Hayles
BOK ... Robert Sloman

and designed and built by the Costume, Make-Up and
Special Effects departments of the BBC.

The Publishers are grateful to the
following actors and actresses, or their
agents, who have given permission for the
reproduction of certain photographs:

Eric L'Epine Smith Ltd for William Hartnell
Patrick Troughton
Jon Pertwee
Tom Baker
Miss Elisabeth Sladen
Mrs Kismet Delgado for Roger Delgado
Donald Gee
Miss Caroline John
Miss Jacqueline Hill
William Russell
Miss Carole Ann Ford

Please note: The Publishers have made every effort
to trace the owners of copyright material in this book.

written by Terrance Dicks

By arrangement with the British Broadcasting Corporation

64